The Canal
Diggers

Stories linking with the History
National Curriculum Key Stage 2.

First published in 1999 by Franklin Watts
96 Leonard Street, London EC2A 4XD

Text © Jon Blake 1999
Illustrations © Kate Sheppard 1999

The right of Jon Blake to be identified as
the Author of this Work has been asserted by
him in accordance with the Copyright, Designs
and Patents Act, 1988

Editor: Claire Berridge
Designer: Jason Anscomb
Consultant: Dr Anne Millard, BA Hons, Dip Ed, PhD

A CIP catalogue record for this book
is available from the British Library.

ISBN 0 7496 3356 5 (hbk)
       0 7496 3545 2 (pbk)

Dewey Classification 386/942.7081

Printed in Great Britain

The Canal Diggers

by Jon Blake

Illustrations by Kate Sheppard

FRANKLIN WATTS
NEW YORK • LONDON • SYDNEY

1

'A Great Historic Day'

Father dashed a bill to his desk. His bald head gleamed purple and his long side-whiskers quivered.

"Damn railways!" he stormed. "They're trying to bleed me dry!"

Father glared from the window

towards the gates of his factory and the sign that read JOSEPH HARPER – MANUFACTURER OF HIGH-QUALITY COTTON UNDERWEAR.

We'll be bust within a month," he snarled. "What with the cost of using the railways, and then the cost of using Liverpool Docks!"

I really wanted to be helpful, but I was only eight, and I didn't understand much about business.

"Can't you complain?" I asked.

"Complain?" scoffed father. "They'd laugh in my face! See, lad, they've got me where they want me. I've got to get cotton to the factory, and I've got to get my long-johns onto the ships. Understand?"

I nodded eagerly. Father began to pace the room.

"If only Manchester was a port! he

said. My costs would be halved!"

"But Manchester's nowhere near the sea," I pointed out.

"Not yet," replied father, with a strange little smile.

It was 1882 when we had this conversation, and I spent the next five years puzzling over what father meant. Were they going to move Manchester? Was the sea going to rise up and swallow

Liverpool?

Then one day, father was unusually excited.

"Today," he proclaimed, "is a Great Historic Day. The day work begins on the Manchester Ship Canal!"

"The what?" I replied.

"The greatest waterway Britain will ever see!" raved father. "A canal so deep and wide, the greatest ships can sail down it! A canal which will make Manchester the greatest port in the world!"

Soon everyone was talking about this Manchester Ship Canal, and important

men from the project were visiting us almost every day. After I'd gone to bed they got out the cigars and talked grown-up talk about imports and exports and who had

aces and a king.

One morning, after one of these late-night parties, father called me into his study.

"Albert," he said. "As you are now on your summer holiday, I have a most important job for you."

Father reached into his inside pocket, took out his wallet, and blew a little dust from it. With a deadly serious expression, he pulled out a pound note.

"I want you to take this pound note," he said, "and give it to Mr Walter

Bradshaw, who is one of the assistant engineers working on the canal."

My head began to spin. Father had

never trusted me with money before. I had a habit of losing things.

"But ... why don't you take it? I asked.

"I shall be in London for the next week on business," replied father.

"Then why doesn't Edwin take it?" I asked. Edwin was our footman.

Father began to look rattled. "It is your duty to obey your father," he barked. "Not to question him."

I took the pound note. A pound was a lot of money – more than father's workers earned in a week. Father told me which pocket to put it in, and where to find Mr Walter Bradshaw, and a few other things which I was too dizzy to take in. Finally he gave me a solemn warning.

"Stay clear of the NAVVIES," he said.

"What are navvies?" I asked nervously.

"Navvies," replied father, "are the

Scum of the Earth!"

"But what *are* they?" I repeated.

"The men with the shovels," replied father. "The men who dig the canal. Thieves, drunkards and brawlers. They come from all parts, like flies to a rotting corpse, and leave behind them a trail of violence and sin."

These frightening words were still echoing in my head as I set off for the canal.

2

The Canal

Mr Walter Bradshaw was working at the
Manchester end of the canal, at a place
called Mode Wheel. I knew Mode Wheel.
One of my aunts lived there. Except, when
I got there, I didn't recognise a thing. A
great scar cut across the land. New

railway lines were everywhere. And as I got closer, an incredible machine came into view. It sat on the railway line, taller than a house, with a chimney belching smoke, and a great wheel pulling up endless buckets from the ground below. The buckets dumped the earth into a railway wagon and the whole thing wheezed and rumbled like the devil's own guts.

I don't know how long I stood staring at this thing, but I do remember the sun was very hot and I had to take off my jacket. I vaguely recall putting it down over the side of a railway wagon but after that I only had eyes for the endless buckets.

Eventually the machine stopped. At this point an engine jerked into life and the wagons full of soil trundled off down the track.

I snapped back to life. Now – where was my jacket?

God help me! The train!

There was nothing I could do. The last wagon was vanishing round the bend. My jacket was on its way to God-knows-where, and so was father's precious pound.

I sank to my knees, desperately trying to decide what to do. There was no way I could go home without paying Mr Walter Bradshaw. Father would kill me, or worse. A crazy plan came to me. I would earn another pound. I would offer myself to Mr Walter Bradshaw for work.

3

Who Wants To Be A Navvy?

Mr Walter Bradshaw looked me up and down and did not seem impressed. I hadn't mentioned that I was Joseph Harper's son, in case he asked for his pound.

"Let me get this clear," he said. "You

want to be the assistant engineer's assistant?"

"That's right," I said. "But I will settle for being his assistant's assistant."

Mr Walter Bradshaw did not laugh. "So tell me," he said. "What do you know about building canals?"

"Well," I said. "You dig a big, big ditch ... then you fill it with water."

"Is that so?" replied Mr Bradshaw.

"More or less," I answered.

"But Manchester is four hundred feet higher than the sea," said Mr Bradshaw. "How do you intend to make water flow up hill?"

"Er ...'

"That's just the first of your problems," said Mr Bradshaw. "Believe me, there are many more."

"I can learn!" I blurted.

"The way to learn," said Mr Bradshaw, "is to start at the bottom, like I did. I started as a stonemason."

"Right," I said. "I'll do that."

I wasn't exactly sure what a stonemason did, but I'd always liked stones, particularly the flat ones that you skim across the river. So I said farewell to Mr Bradshaw and set off to find one. A stonemason that is, not a stone! I was directed to Weaste, where

they were building a wharf, which is a place to unload ships.

It took an age to get to Weaste, but it

didn't take long to find a stonemason. His name was Will, but he wasn't very willing.

"So," he said, with a dour look. "You want to be a stonemason, do you?"

"That's right," I replied brightly.

"Know how to dress a stone?" he asked.

"I never knew that stones wore dresses!" I replied.

Will gave me a long weary look and that was the end of my interview. But just as I was trudging away dejected, to my surprise, he called me back.

"They're looking for men down at

Trafford," he said.

"Stonemasons?" I asked, hopefully.

"Not stonemasons," he replied.
"Navvies."

4

A New Job

Yes, I know what father said. But just because I was going to be a navvy, it didn't mean I had to be a drunkard, a brawler and a rotting fly, or whatever it was. I would keep myself to myself, not talk to a soul, and get the job done as quickly as possible.

Reaching Barton I asked a few questions and got directed to a rough wooden hut. Inside was a stocky, red-faced man at a desk, scribbling on a piece of paper.

"I've heard you've got some jobs," I said, brightly.

"My name is Mister Harris," growled the man, looking up. "But you can call me Sir."

"I've heard you've got some jobs, sir," I repeated.

"Are you fit?" he grunted, laying down his quill.

"I think so. Sir."

Mr Harris looked doubtful. "We don't want shirkers," he said. "It's hard graft. Ten hours a day, six days a week."

Ten hours a day? I was feeling tired already! "How much do you pay, sir?" I asked.

"Three and fourpence."

"An hour? That's good!"

"A day, you cheeky monkey!"

I worked it out. Yes, I should clear a pound in a week. One week's hard labour, and it would all be over.

"Shall I start now, sir?" I asked.

"What, in those clothes?"

"What's wrong with them, sir?"

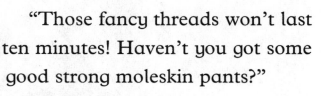

"Those fancy threads won't last ten minutes! Haven't you got some good strong moleskin pants?"

Whatskin pants?"

Mr Harris gave an impatient sigh. "Wait there!" he barked, strolling out. In a few minutes he was back, carrying a full set of (very dirty) clothes over his arm.

"You can wear these." he barked.

I took the clothes. There was a thick cotton shirt (no collar), a rough pair of corduroy trousers and a matching waistcoat, all topped off with a flat cap. A smell of mud and grown man's sweat wafted up to my nostrils.

"But whose are they?" I asked.

"Never mind," said Mr Harris. "He'll have no need of them now."

5

Frosty

Mr Harris took me down to the place I would be working. I looked down into a monster cutting. At least a hundred men were slaving away down there. Long wooden ramps led to the top of the cutting. Men were making their way up

these wooden ramps with wheelbarrows.
Each wheelbarrow was fixed to a rope,

which went up the ramp, over a pulley, and onto a horse. The horses slowly pulled the men and the barrows up to the top, where they were emptied into railway wagons.

I looked over the edge and watched a man coming up, but not for long. The ramp was narrow and the drop was awesome. My head swam.

Luckily, there was another way into the cutting. Mr Harris led me down through the masses of sweating workers and stopped at a tall, hard-faced man with frown-lines as deep as furrows in a field. His eyes were flat at the top, like a gull's, and he wore a huge walrus moustache which almost hid two big rabbity front teeth.

"Got a nipper for you, Sam," said Mr Harris.

In reply, the walrus man hawked
something terrible up into his throat and
spat on the ground.

"This is Mr Frost, your foreman," Mr
Harris said to me. "As far as you're
concerned, his word is law. You got that?"

"Yes, sir," I peeped.

Mr Harris left and the walrus man
handed me a pickaxe and a spade. "Fill

that," he said, pointing to a nearby barrow.

I could sense all the eyes turning towards me. I swung back my pickaxe. It was amazingly heavy. So heavy, in fact, that it swung me straight off my feet and sent me crashing down backwards. There was a huge roar of laughter. I tried again,

more carefully. The pickaxe hardly made a dent in the ground, which was full of stones and as hard as iron.

"Ach!" shouted one man. "You've got to give it more than that, nipper!"

I pretended that I hadn't heard, and did the same again.

"Oy!" came the same voice. "Nipper! Are you deaf?" the man said as he patted me on the shoulder.

This gave me a great idea. I turned to my audience and, with the aid of a few hand-signals, mimed that I was indeed deaf. They asked me if it happened when they were blasting rock, and I nodded eagerly, and they looked quite sorry, and I felt a bit guilty. Especially when they started talking about me.

"Look at those hands," said one voice. "Softer than a milkmaid's."

"He won't last a week," said another.

I don't know how long it took me to fill my barrow, but everyone else seemed to have filled six. It was such a relief that I took a little sit-down. When the foreman caught sight of me doing that his eyes blazed  and his boots bore down on me like thunder.

"Don't you sit down on the job!" he

roared. "Get up that barrow-run!"

I quickly checked that no-one was listening. "What's a barrow-run?" I whispered.

"That, you idiot!" cried Mr Frost. To my horror, he pointed straight at one of the ramps I'd seen earlier. From where I

was now, it seemed even steeper. Pure fear ran through my veins.

"But … I'm afraid of heights," I whispered.

As soon as I said it, I wished I hadn't. A cruel glint came into old Frosty's eyes. He closed my hands round the handles of the barrow, half-dragged me to the barrow-run, and tied the rope around the front axle.

"Do you know what I do with chickens?" he grunted.

"No, sir," I replied.

"I roast 'em," snarled Frosty.

"Do you?" I replied.

"Now get up that faffing run!" he barked, except he didn't actually say 'faffing'!

I pushed the barrow onto the planks. Frosty shouted up, a man answered, the rope went tight, and the barrow started going up. I tried to concentrate on my feet, but I could still see the ground getting further and further away. Fear turned to terror and terror turned to horror. I wasn't going to make it! If I went any higher, I was going over the edge!

In a blind panic I let go of the barrow and ran back down. The barrow swung off the edge of the ramp and the whole load of earth

and stones rained down on the men below.
The air was suddenly thick with swear
words, and I was surrounded by a sea of
furious faces, none more furious than
Frosty's.

"You ruddy idiot!" he cried, except he
didn't really say 'ruddy'!

"Sorry!" I blurted.

"He's not deaf at all!" someone
shouted.

I clamped a hand over my mouth but

the damage was done. The gang of men moved forward, picks in hand, and I really believed the end was near.

Suddenly a man stepped in front of the gang. He was about fifty, with blond hair and an intelligent face full of worry-lines. "Come on, lads," he said. "He's just a nipper."

The crowd backed away. I breathed again. "Thank you," I said.

"Just be careful," said the blond man. "Everybody's on edge."

"Why's that?" I asked.

Suddenly Frosty appeared between us. "Oy!" he rasped. "You ain't paid to talk! Get back to work!"

6

Hard Graft And Hot Dinners

That first day with the navvies was the
longest of my life. My hands were blistered
and my whole body ached. But there was
no way I could go home, not until I'd paid
Mr Bradshaw his pound.

I sought out the blond man who'd

saved me earlier. He was sitting at the
edge of the cutting, stuffing tobacco into
an old clay pipe. A mate sat silently beside

him, doing the
same. I asked the
blond man why
everybody was
on edge.

"Haven't you
heard?" he said.
"Six men were
killed yesterday."

"H-how?" I asked with a quiver.

"Someone sent the rail trucks the
wrong way," said his mate. "Came right
over the edge."

I started to picture the scene, but not
for long. That accident might have
happened today, and I might have ended
up under those trucks.

"Are there many accidents?" I asked, trying to hide my growing terror.

"Put it this way," replied the man. "They've built three hospitals along these canal works. They didn't build them for nothing!"

We talked some more. I found out that the man's name was Jed, that he had a family down in Bristol, but he tramped all over Britain looking for work. Jed said I reminded him of his eldest son, which was maybe why he was  friendly to me. I was pleased about this, because I was desperate to make friends.

"Are you all off to get drunk now?" I asked, trying to sound big.

Jed looked at me as if I was mad. "I'm

off to get a good hot meal, myself," he
said. "Where are you lodging, nipper?"

"Lodging?" I replied. "Nowhere."

"Sleeping in a ditch, are you?" asked
Jed's mate.

I didn't know what to say. I suddenly
felt ashamed of living in a big town house
with a housekeeper and red velvet
curtains.

"That's right," I said. "I'm sleeping in
a ditch."

"You'd better come with us," said Jed.

7

Life As A Navvy

Jed and his mate Bob stayed in the strangest lodging-house I'd ever seen. It was an old barge converted into a big floating shed, with hard wooden beds and a pot-bellied stove. The navvies crammed themselves round a crude table while Mrs Aston, the one woman

on board, served them their suppers. As
the evening wore on, and the men told
their endless tales under the dim gas-light,
a homely feeling came over me. I even told
my own story, which got the biggest laugh
of all. That night I slept as sound as a
princess on a feather bed.

Next morning I sent a letter home
telling the staff not to worry about me as I
was staying with my Aunt for the week (of
course I wasn't really!), and then I got
back to the site, determined to make a

fresh start. I tipped my cap to Frosty and bade him good morning.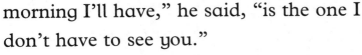

"You trying to be funny?" he snarled.

"Just saying good morning," I replied.

Frosty brought his face up close to mine.

"The only good morning I'll have," he said, "is the one I don't have to see you."

Frosty had a special punishment for me because I was afraid of the barrow-runs. It was my job to break up the boulders. Jed had told me to love the boulders because the digging machines couldn't handle them, so they kept us in work. But after a few hours of chipping away with my pickaxe, my love for the boulders was wearing thin. I felt like I was a machine myself, but not a very good one.

I don't know how I got through that second day. After that, however, the days all seemed the same, and I couldn't really tell if I'd been working an hour or a month. I started to talk like the other navvies, and even sing their songs. I got to know loads of the men: the jokers, the moaners, the friendly ones and the vicious headcases. I looked forward to the lunch breaks when we could have a laugh and a gripe, usually about Frosty.

But there was one big difference between me and the others. I was finishing on Saturday.

8

Barrow-run Antics

It was Friday night when the rain began.
It started as a drizzle and turned into a
downpour. I listened to it rattle on the tin
roof of the houseboat and my heart sank.

"Will we still have to work?" I asked.

"No work, no pay," replied Jed.

The men were nervous of the rains. A few months before a dam had burst and some men had drowned. Work was always more dangerous in the rain.

Next morning the rain was still falling and the cutting was ankle deep in water. The men looked anxiously at the slippery

barrow-runs. But Frosty was not going to make things any easier for us.

"What's the matter, nipper?" he snarled. "You never been out in the rain before?"

I got to work. If the job was hard before, it was murder now. There was no singing from Jed and Bob today.

As the day wore on, and the rain poured harder, tempers got frayed. There were arguments all over the place. Then, halfway through the afternoon, there was an almighty row. Frosty got involved. Next thing, two men had walked off the job. As they climbed out of sight, Frosty looked round for someone to take it out on. I put my head down quickly. For a moment I thought I'd escaped. Then those big brown boots splashed down in front of me.

"Having a good laugh?" rasped Frosty.

No, sir," I replied. "I wasn't laughing at all."

There was a short menacing silence.

"I've been too soft on you," said Frosty. "Get up that barrow-run."

I was seized with terror. The ramps were dangerous before the rain – now they were murder. Jed's words came back to me: "They didn't build those hospitals for nothing".

"Are you deaf?" shouted Frosty.

I took hold of the handles of my barrow and began to trudge through the mud. Frosty tied the rope to the barrow

and shouted up. As the rope tightened, I
struggled up onto the ramp, desperately
trying to keep my footing. The ramp was
covered in slippery wet clay, and every step
was dangerous. But I was tougher now. I
kept my eyes fixed ahead and took one
step at a time. Halfway ... three-quarters
... rain driving in my face ... nearly there
... at last!

I stood at the top of the cutting,
fighting for breath, as the barrow was
emptied into a waiting truck. For a second
I was eye to eye with a steaming carthorse,

and in that second I thought, that's how they see us. No more than animals.

But the hardest part was still to come. I had to wheel the barrow back down. And the second I looked over the edge, I knew I couldn't do it. My knees swam and my head turned to jelly.

"What are you waiting for?" screamed Frosty.

I stayed frozen to the spot.

"Get down here now!" screamed Frosty.

Slowly I shook my head. Next second, Frosty was scrabbling his way furiously up the barrow-run. Once at the top, he

pushed me full in the chest and grabbed
my barrow.

"You're pathetic, lad!" he snarled.
"Pathetic!"

As Frosty turned his back, a monstrous
anger welled up
in me, and as he
set off down the
ramp, I could
control myself no
longer. With a
swift hook from
my right foot, I

took his legs from under him. The barrow
crashed over the edge and Frosty tumbled
like a circus clown all the way down the
ramp and SPLAT! into the mud at the
bottom.

Suddenly the whole cutting was silent.
Every single man had stopped work.

My new career, needless to say, was over.

Ah well, I thought. It was my last day anyway. All I had to do was wait a few hours, then collect my wages.

Or so I thought.

"Harper," grunted Mr Harris, as I finally reached the pay desk. "Two and six."

I stared down at the measly half crown

that Mr Harris handed me. This couldn't be right!

"I'm supposed to get over a pound!" I protested.

"Yes," said Mr Harris. "But you've had eighteen shillings deducted."

"What?" I cried.

"Two shillings for the hours you missed, and sixteen to replace Mr Frost's clothes."

"You can't do that!" I cried.

"Next!" said Mr Harris.

I was powerless. I didn't know the law, I wasn't in a union, and I couldn't run to father. I sloped away in total despair. All this for nothing!

I don't know how long I sat behind the hut, watching the men talk about the night ahead and the wild time they were going to have. All that was ahead of me was a sad walk home and my father's furious face.

Then, out of the blue, a hand landed

on my shoulder. I turned to see Jed and Bob.

"Here you go, lad," said Jed.

To my amazement, Jed held out a pile of coins. Before I could stop him he tipped the lot into my hands. At a rough count, I was holding about eighteen shillings.

"We've had a whip round," said Jed.

"Couldn't see you going short," added Bob.

It didn't make sense to me. The navvies were poor enough as it was.

"I can't take this," I said.

"You are taking it," said Jed.

"What you did to Frosty," added Bob, "you did for all of us."

With that, Bob slapped me on the back, Jed ruffled my hair, and I knew I had two friends for life.

I thanked them both and rushed off to find Mr Walter Bradshaw before anything

could happen to the money they had
given me!

It was with great relief that I finally
handed over the pound to Mr Bradshaw.
For some strange reason he was a lot
happier to see me this time! As he
pocketed the money, he muttered
something about people shouldn't gamble
if they couldn't pay their debts back
straight away. I wasn't really sure what he
meant, but it definitely didn't sound like
something I should ask father about.

9

The Manchester Ship Canal

On New Year's Day 1894, the Manchester
Ship Canal was opened. I stood beside
father at Salford Docks as the *Norseman*
steamed in, with a whole procession of
ships behind.

Needless to say, father was a happy

man. He wore his very best suit and stood tall. I remembered the time when I had looked up to him and thought he was such a great man. Funny, he didn't seem so great these days.

"Look at that!" he proclaimed. "And they said we'd never do it!"

I smiled to myself. The fact was that father hadn't done anything. It was Jed and Bob and all the others who'd built that canal. With a little help from me of course!

Notes

The Manchester Ship Canal was built between 1887 and 1893. It was 36 miles long, from the estuary of the River Mersey to the docks at Salford. To build it, 70 million tons of rock and earth had to be moved.

The man in charge of building the Manchester Ship Canal was Thomas Walker. He was keen to use machines wherever possible, such as 'Steam navvies' (diggers), cranes, pumps and dredgers. He also used temporary railways to carry workers and materials to and fro. However, he died in 1889, before the canal was completed.

Up to 17, 000 men were employed building the canal. These included navvies,

bricklayers, carpenters, masons, engine drivers and the men who drove the cranes and excavators.

The men building the canal had to overcome many problems. The canal cut through several roads and even another canal. Ordinary bridges would have been too low for ships to pass under, so 'swing bridges' had to be built. They could swing to one side to allow ships to pass.

The most amazing bridge of all was the Barton Swing Aqueduct. This lifted a whole section of the old Bridgewater Canal out of the way of boats on the new Ship Canal. The Swing Aqueduct was like a huge bath full of water – sometimes it would be swung round with a barge still in it, and a horse pulling the barge!

There were many disasters during the building of the Manchester Ship Canal. Floods were common, often destroying the new workings. So were accidents from the new machines and railway equipment. 130 men died during the building of the canal. 163 were permanently disabled. Another 1,000 had other accidents.

The workers on the canal had few rights. If worked stopped because of flooding, for example, they would simply be thrown out of work. However, they did not take everything lying down. In 1890 they threatened a mass strike which led to an increase in pay.

Once opened, the Manchester Ship Canal proved a major success for the businessmen of Manchester: it turned an inland city into one of Britain's leading ports.

Sparks: Historical Adventures

ANCIENT GREECE
The Great Horse of Troy – The Trojan War
0 7496 3369 7 (hbk)   0 7496 3538 X (pbk)
The Winner's Wreath – Ancient Greek Olympics
0 7496 3368 9 (hbk)   0 7496 3555 X (pbk)

INVADERS AND SETTLERS
Viking Raiders – A Norse Attack
0 7496 3089 2 (hbk)   0 7496 3457 X (pbk)
Boudica Strikes Back – The Romans in Britain
0 7496 3366 2 (hbk)   0 7496 3546 0 (pbk)
Erik's New Home – A Viking Town
0 7496 3367 0 (hbk)   0 7496 3552 5 (pbk)
TALES OF THE ROWDY ROMANS
The Great Necklace Hunt
0 7496 2221 0 (hbk)   0 7496 2628 3 (pbk)
The Lost Legionary
0 7496 2222 9 (hbk)   0 7496 2629 1 (pbk)
The Guard Dog Geese
0 7496 2331 4 (hbk)   0 7496 2630 5 (pbk)
A Runaway Donkey
0 7496 2332 2 (hbk)   0 7496 2631 3 (pbk)

TUDORS AND STUARTS
Captain Drake's Orders – The Armada
0 7496 2556 2 (hbk)   0 7496 3121 X (pbk)
London's Burning – The Great Fire of London
0 7496 2557 0 (hbk)   0 7496 3122 8 (pbk)
Mystery at the Globe – Shakespeare's Theatre
0 7496 3096 5 (hbk)   0 7496 3449 9 (pbk)
Stranger in the Glen – Rob Roy
0 7496 2586 4 (hbk)   0 7496 3123 6 (pbk)
A Dream of Danger – The Massacre of Glencoe
0 7496 2587 2 (hbk)   0 7496 3124 4 (pbk)
A Queen's Promise – Mary Queen of Scots
0 7496 2589 9 (hbk)   0 7496 3125 2 (pbk)
Over the Sea to Skye – Bonnie Prince Charlie
0 7496 2588 0 (hbk)   0 7496 3126 0 (pbk)
Plague! – A Tudor Epidemic
0 7496 3365 4 (hbk)   0 7496 3556 8 (pbk)
TALES OF A TUDOR TEARAWAY
A Pig Called Henry
0 7496 2204 4 (hbk)   0 7496 2625 9 (pbk)
A Horse Called Deathblow
0 7496 2205 9 (hbk)   0 7496 2624 0 (pbk)
Dancing for Captain Drake
0 7496 2234 2 (hbk)   0 7496 2626 7 (pbk)
Birthdays are a Serious Business
0 7496 2235 0 (hbk)   0 7496 2627 5 (pbk)

VICTORIAN ERA
The Runaway Slave – The British Slave Trade
0 7496 3093 0 (hbk)   0 7496 3456 1 (pbk)
The Sewer Sleuth – Victorian Cholera
0 7496 2590 2 (hbk)   0 7496 3128 7 (pbk)
Convict! – Criminals Sent to Australia
0 7496 2591 0 (hbk)   0 7496 3129 5 (pbk)
An Indian Adventure – Victorian India
0 7496 3090 6 (hbk)   0 7496 3451 0 (pbk)
Farewell to Ireland – Emigration to America
0 7496 3094 9 (hbk)   0 7496 3448 0 (pbk)

The Great Hunger – Famine in Ireland
0 7496 3095 7 (hbk)   0 7496 3447 2 (pbk)
Fire Down the Pit – A Welsh Mining Disaster
0 7496 3091 4 (hbk)   0 7496 3450 2 (pbk)
Tunnel Rescue – The Great Western Railway
0 7496 3353 0 (hbk)   0 7496 3537 1 (pbk)
Kidnap on the Canal – Victorian Waterways
0 7496 3352 2 (hbk)   0 7496 3540 1 (pbk)
Dr. Barnardo's Boys – Victorian Charity
0 7496 3358 1 (hbk)   0 7496 3541 X (pbk)
The Iron Ship – Brunel's Great Britain
0 7496 3355 7 (hbk)   0 7496 3543 6 (pbk)
Bodies for Sale – Victorian Tomb-Robbers
0 7496 3364 6 (hbk)   0 7496 3539 8 (pbk)
Penny Post Boy – The Victorian Postal Service
0 7496 3362 X (hbk)   0 7496 3544 4 (pbk)
The Canal Diggers – The Manchester Ship Canal
0 7496 3356 5 (hbk)   0 7496 3545 2 (pbk)
The Tay Bridge Tragedy – A Victorian Disaster
0 7496 3354 9 (hbk)   0 7496 3547 9 (pbk)
Stop, Thief! – The Victorian Police
0 7496 3359 X (hbk)   0 7496 3548 7 (pbk)
Miss Buss and Miss Beale – Victorian Schools
0 7496 3360 3 (hbk)   0 7496 3549 5 (pbk)
Chimney Charlie – Victorian Chimney Sweeps
0 7496 3351 4 (hbk)   0 7496 3551 7 (pbk)
Down the Drain – Victorian Sewers
0 7496 3357 3 (hbk)   0 7496 3550 9 (pbk)
The Ideal Home – A Victorian New Town
0 7496 3361 1 (hbk)   0 7496 3553 3 (pbk)
Stage Struck – Victorian Music Hall
0 7496 3363 8 (hbk)   0 7496 3554 1 (pbk)
TRAVELS OF A YOUNG VICTORIAN
The Golden Key
0 7496 2360 8 (hbk)   0 7496 2632 1 (pbk)
Poppy's Big Push
0 7496 2361 6 (hbk)   0 7496 2633 X (pbk)
Poppy's Secret
0 7496 2374 8 (hbk)   0 7496 2634 8 (pbk)
The Lost Treasure
0 7496 2375 6 (hbk)   0 7496 2635 6 (pbk)

20th-CENTURY HISTORY
Fight for the Vote – The Suffragettes
0 7496 3092 2 (hbk)   0 7496 3452 9 (pbk)
The Road to London – The Jarrow March
0 7496 2609 7 (hbk)   0 7496 3132 5 (pbk)
The Sandbag Secret – The Blitz
0 7496 2608 9 (hbk)   0 7496 3133 3 (pbk)
Sid's War – Evacuation
0 7496 3209 7 (hbk)   0 7496 3445 6 (pbk)
D-Day! – Wartime Adventure
0 7496 3208 9 (hbk)   0 7496 3446 4 (pbk)
The Prisoner – A Prisoner of War
0 7496 3212 7 (hbk)   0 7496 3455 3 (pbk)
Escape from Germany – Wartime Refugees
0 7496 3211 9 (hbk)   0 7496 3454 5 (pbk)
Flying Bombs – Wartime Bomb Disposal
0 7496 3210 0 (hbk)   0 7496 3453 7 (pbk)
12,000 Miles From Home – Sent to Australia
0 7496 3370 0 (hbk) 0 7496 3542 8 (pbk)